For Celia

Library of Congress Cataloging in Publication Data

Hughes, Shirley.
   Colors.
   Summary: Rhyming text introduces the colors of familiar
objects and special places.
   [1. Color — Fiction. 2. Stories in rhyme]   I. Title.
PZ8.3.H8665Co   1986   [E]   86-2732
ISBN 0-688-04206-6

Colors

Shirley Hughes

LOTHROP, LEE & SHEPARD BOOKS
NEW YORK

blue

Baby blues, navy blues, blue socks, blue shoes.

Blue plate, blue mug, blue flowers in a blue jug.

And fluffy white clouds floating by
in a great big beautiful bright blue sky.

yellow

Syrup dripping from a spoon,

buttercups,

a harvest moon.

Sun like honey on the floor,
warm as the steps by our back door.

red

Rosy apples, dark cherries,

scarlet leaves, bright berries.

And when the winter's day is done,
a fiery sky, a big red sun.

red and yellow make

orange

Tangerines and apricots,
orange flowers in orange pots.

Orange glow on an orange mat,
marmalade toast and a marmalade cat.

blue and red make

purple

Berries in the bramble patch.
Pick them (but mind the thorns don't scratch)!

Purple blossom, pale and dark,
spreading with springtime in the park.

blue and yellow make

green

Grasshoppers, greenflies, gooseberries, cat's eyes.

Green lettuce, green peas,

green shade from green trees.
And grass as far as you can see
like green waves in a green sea.

black

Shiny boots,
a witch's hat.
Black cloak,
black cat.

Black crows cawing high,
winter trees against the sky.

white

Thistledown like white fluff,
dandelion clocks to puff.
White cover on my bed,
white pillow for my head.

White snowflakes, whirling down,
covering gardens, roofs, and town.